Bennett Cerf's
Book of
Riddles

Illustrated by Roy Mc Kie

BEGINNER BOOKS
A Division of Random House, Inc.

Why do birds fly south?

Because it is too far to walk.

What gets lost every time
you stand up?

Your lap.

6

What kind of dog has no tail?

A hot dog.

What is the last thing you
take off when you go to bed?

You take your feet off the floor.

What do giraffes have that no other animals have?

Little giraffes.

Why does the fireman wear
red suspenders?

To keep his pants up.

Why did the little boy throw
the clock out the window?

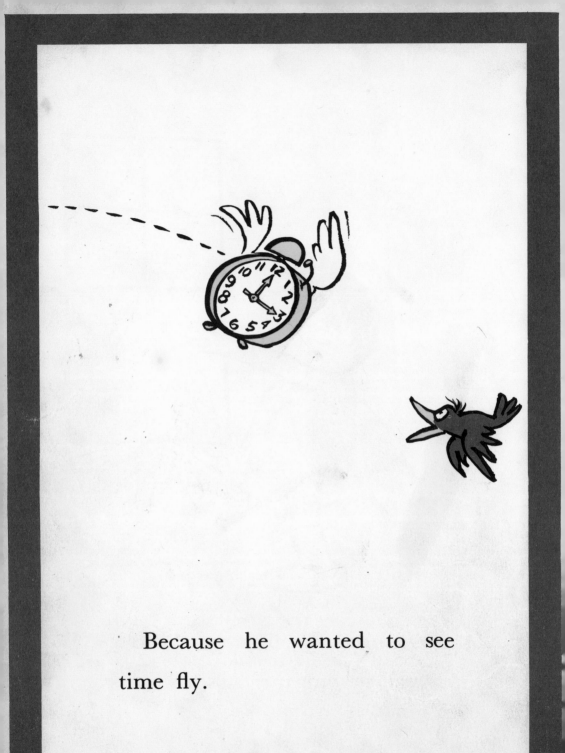

Because he wanted to see time fly.

What is the best way to
make a fire with two sticks?

Make sure one of the sticks is a match.

What time is it when an elephant sits on a fence?

Time to get a new fence.

What did the big firecracker
say to the little firecracker?

"My pop is bigger than your pop."

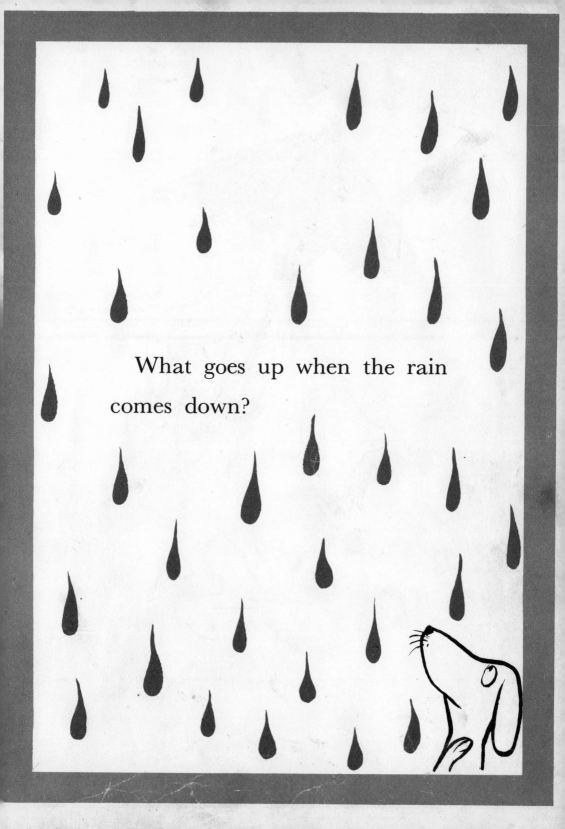

What goes up when the rain comes down?

An umbrella.

What kind of animals can jump higher than a house?

All kinds of animals. Houses
can not jump.

What holds up a train?

What is a bird after he is four days old?

Five days old.

What is the first thing you
put in a garden?

Your foot.

Why is an egg not like an elephant?

If you do not know, I would not want to send you to get eggs.

What dog keeps the best time?

A watch dog.

Why do white sheep eat so
much more than black sheep?

Because there are so many
more white sheep.

What is big and red and eats rocks?

A big red rock eater.

How many lions can you
put in an empty cage?

One. After that the cage is
not empty.

How many balls of string
would it take to reach the
moon?

Just one. But it would have
to be a big one.

Why does a hen lay eggs?

Because if she let them drop,
they would break.

What makes more noise than
a cat stuck in a tree?

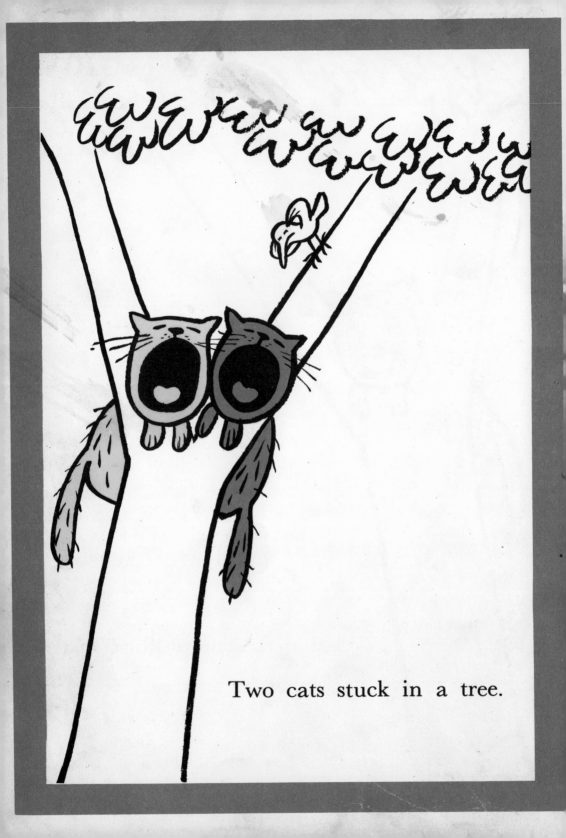

Two cats stuck in a tree.

Why does a baby pig eat so much?

To make a hog of himself.

If you drop a white hat into the Red Sea, what will it become?

Wet.

What kind of animal has a head like a cat and a tail like a cat, but is not a cat?

A kitten.

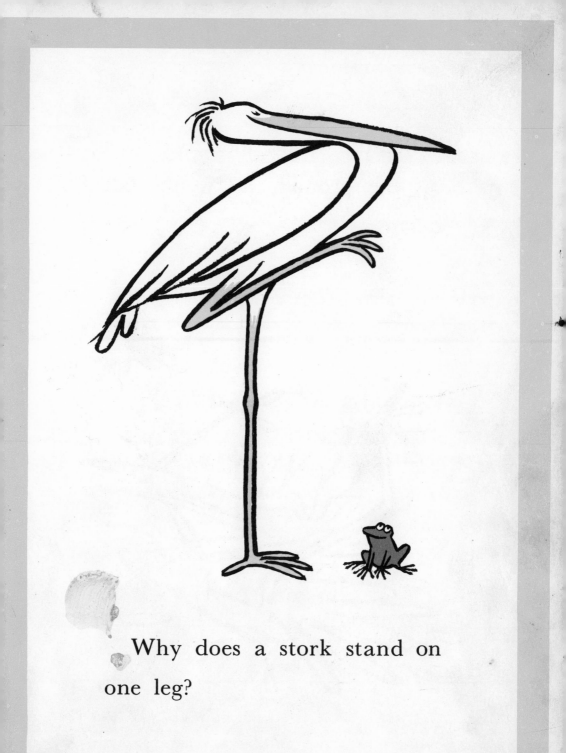

Why does a stork stand on one leg?

Because if he took two legs
off the ground, he would fall
down.

Name five things that have milk in them.

MILK

Butter.

Cheese.

Ice Cream.

And two cows.

Who always goes to bed
with his shoes on?

A horse.

When is a cook bad?

When he beats an egg.

What did the pig say when
a man got him by the tail?

The pig said, "This is the
end of me."